This Orchard book belongs to

____

____

To Ella, Andrew and Lorna - JS

ORCHARD BOOKS
Carmelite House
50 Victoria Embankment
London EC4Y 0DZ

First published in 2012 by Orchard Books

First paperback publication in 2013

ISBN 978 1 40831 854 6

A CIP catalogue record for this book is available from the British Library.

2 4 6 8 10 9 7 5 3

Printed in China

Orchard Books
An imprint of Hachette Children's Group
Part of The Watts Publishing Group Limited
An Hachette UK Company

www.hachette.co.uk

Lily Gets Lost!

Jane Simmons

ORCHARD

Spring was in the air
and everything was buzzing.
When Lily heard a nibbling
behind the hedge she thought,
"Who could nibble such a nibble?"

Lily had to see.

She pushed through the hedge
and there, on the other side, was a rabbit,
ears twitching and nose wiggling.

Lily twitched and wiggled too.

Hippity, hop, hopped the rabbit.
Lily hopped too,
around the orchard with all the rabbits.

Hippity, hoppity,
hippity, hop!

When Lily heard a snort
behind the bushes she thought,
"Who could snort such a snort?"
Lily had to see.

"Mooo! Mooo! Mooo!" mooed the cows.
Lily mooed too, "Mooo!"

Mooo!

Lily heard a splash behind the reeds.
Who could splosh such a splash?
Lily had to see.

“Quack! Quack! Quack!” quacked the ducks.
Lily quacked too, “Quack!”
But all the ducklings raced back to their mamma,

and suddenly Lily missed her mamma too.
Where was Mamma?
Lily had to see . . .

. . . was Mamma here?
No, there were only donkeys in the paddock.
"Eey-or, EEY-OR!" they bellowed so loudly it frightened her.
"MAAAA?" Lily cried and ran away
as fast as she could.

Eey-or!
EEY-OR!

Was Mamma here?
"MAA MAAAA!" Lily called,
but a deep rumble came from the shadows.

Grrrrunt!

Lily gasped!
Who could grunt such a grunt?

MAAAAAA!

Lily didn't want to see!
"MAAAAAA! MAAA!" Lily wailed.

"Grunt, oink, grunt," went the piglets.
"Shush now!" grunted Mamma Pig, kindly, and the piglets shushed. And Lily shushed.
The barn fell silent and noises from outside floated in, an eey-or, a splash and a snort.

"Listen carefully now," said Mamma Pig.
Lily listened carefully past the quack, past the moo,
and far, far away she heard a "Baa! Baa! Baaa!"
Who could baa such a baa?

"Mammaaa!" she cried and ran out of the barn,

past the

Eey-or!

past the

QUACK!

past the **Mooo!**

past the

Hoppity, hop!

and through the hedge . . .

. . . all the way back to Mamma.
“Lily!” said Mamma. “Where have you been?”
And Lily thought, “Oink, eey-or, quack, mooo!”
but all she could say was . . .

"Maa! Maa! Maa!"